The Boy Who Cried Wolf
A Tale of Honesty

The Boy Who Cried Wolf
A Tale of Honesty

Illustrated by Jon Goodell

Adapted by Mary Rowitz

Publications International, Ltd.

There was a young boy who lived in a village. He wasn't very old, but he had an important job. He was a shepherd, and his job was to guard the sheep from danger, especially wolves.

The shepherd boy also had to make sure the sheep got plenty of food and exercise. Every day the boy walked the sheep to a nearby valley. There the sheep would graze on the valley's tasty green grass. The villagers trusted the shepherd to take good care of the sheep.

The shepherd boy wasn't really all alone. The village people worked nearby. If a wolf ever did attack, the people could run to the rescue.

The villagers counted on the shepherd boy to do his job. They never felt like they had to check on him. They trusted him to do what he was supposed to do.

Every day the shepherd faithfully watched the sheep from his lookout post. He could also see the people hard at work. Some days they worked at their jobs in the village. Sometimes they did other chores.

For the shepherd boy, every day was the same. He looked at the sheep. They looked the same every day. Then he looked out at the forest. It looked the same, too. While he was happy most days just to do his job, some days he wished that something exciting would happen.

In his whole life, the boy had never seen a wolf come near the sheep. In fact, he had never even seen a wolf! Some people told stories of hearing wolves howl in the forest, but the boy never heard howling. Sometimes he even wondered if there really were any wolves.

One day the shepherd tried to make things more exciting. He thought, "Maybe I can play some games with the sheep." He planned his next day. He smiled when he thought about the fun he would have.

The boy woke up bright and early the next morning. He ate his breakfast very quickly and then packed his bag for the day. He kissed his parents good-bye and hurried to take the sheep to the valley.

As soon as they reached the green grass in the valley, the shepherd boy tried to play games with the sheep. The sheep, however, had a different idea. They didn't want to play catch. They didn't want to bounce the ball. They didn't even want to try to kick the ball. All the sheep wanted to do was eat the grass or take a nap. "This isn't any fun at all," thought the shepherd boy.

Downhearted, the shepherd boy walked slowly back to his lookout post. "Alas," thought the boy, "I just wanted to make things a little more exciting around here."

Then something caught the corner of his eye. He could tell the wind was blowing because it made the treetops move. "I wonder," he said, thinking out loud, "what is on the other side of those trees?"

The boy smiled to himself. Would it be so bad to pretend there was a wolf? He thought this would be a good joke.

As the sheep ate the grass, he cupped his hand near his mouth and shouted, "Wolf! Wolf! A wolf is stealing the sheep! Come help me!"

All the village people stopped what they were doing. They ran to the valley to help scare off the wolf. When they got there, they were very confused.

The villagers did not find a wolf. They did not even find the shepherd. They were worried about him. What if the wolf had stolen the boy? They frantically began to search high and low to find him.

A villager pointed to a tree and said, "There he is over there. Is he okay?" They saw he was not hurt. In fact, the boy was laughing!

"You looked so funny running up here for no reason. This was a great joke," laughed the boy.

The villagers did not laugh. They had been very scared for the boy and the sheep. They did not feel like laughing at all. They shook their heads and said, "We have to get back to work now. We don't have time for pranks."

The shepherd boy hardly heard a word they said. He was laughing too hard.

At breakfast the next day, the boy's mother and father told him to be good. He nodded his head and left to tend the sheep. Soon, however, he was bored again. "Wolf! Wolf!" he shouted, louder than the day before. "A wolf is stealing the sheep! Come help me!"

Again the villagers came running. Again there was no wolf in sight. This time the village people were very upset. They told the boy, "If you don't tell people the truth all the time, they will never know when to believe you."

The boy was still laughing at his joke. After the villagers went back to their jobs, however, he started to think about what they had said. "Maybe," he thought, "it isn't so funny to play tricks on others." Little did he know he was soon going to have all the excitement he could handle.

Just on the other side of the trees, a sly wolf had seen everything. He watched the boy return to his post and sit comfortably beneath the tree. The wolf knew the boy was not expecting him.

Suddenly the wolf jumped out from behind the trees and began stealing the sheep! The boy couldn't believe his eyes. It was a real wolf! He cried out, "Wolf! Wolf! A wolf is stealing the sheep! Come help me!"

He waited for the villagers to run to his rescue, but no one came. They weren't going to fall for his trick again! This time, though, it was not a trick.

The boy tried yelling for help again, but no one came from the village. He could only watch as the wolf ran into the forest with all the sheep. This time the only one laughing was the wolf.

The shepherd boy ran into the village. "Wolf! Wolf!" he cried. "He's stealing our sheep!" The boy kept running and calling for help, but no one believed he was telling the truth. He called out again, "Wolf! Wolf!"

"I bet!" said one villager. "I can't believe that boy is trying to fool us again."

"Well, he's not going to make a fool out of me," said another villager. "I don't believe him."

The shepherd boy stopped running. "I'm telling the truth this time," he said. "There really is a wolf in the valley, and he really is stealing the sheep. Please believe me."

The villagers came and looked at the boy. They shook their fingers at him. "We're smarter than you think," they said. "This time we're just going to ignore you and your wolf! Humph!"

At that moment, the shepherd boy knew no one would believe him. How could he blame the villagers? When they trusted him, he let them down. He lost their trust by not always telling the truth.

He sadly walked back to his post and gazed down to where he took the sheep to eat grass. There weren't any sheep left. The wolf had taken all of them away. Now the boy was alone. He was so sad that he began to cry.

The boy remembered what his parents and the villagers had told him. How he wished he had listened to them. He wished he had just always told the truth.

He didn't want any harm to come to the sheep! Because he didn't tell the truth, no one believed him when it really mattered. Now it was too late. The boy didn't think his joke was so funny anymore.

One to Grow On
Honesty

The shepherd boy learned the hard way about the importance of being honest. When he played tricks on the villagers, he paid a big price for a small joke. As much fun as it is to laugh, it is always important to tell the truth.

If you were one of the villagers, would you know when to believe the shepherd boy? How do you think it felt to be tricked? What are ways you can be sure people know you are telling the truth?

The End